# Contents

# Dreamtime

Here are dreams – possible and impossible. They are the daydreams we all have in our memories and imaginations, and they describe worlds we can live in and enjoy whenever we choose. They can take you to revisit places and people you used to know, as well as into a future which may, or may not, come true.

## I Saw a Peacock

I saw a Peacock with a fiery tail,
I saw a blazing Comet drop down hail,
I saw a Cloud with ivy circled round,
I saw a sturdy Oak creep on the ground,
I saw a Pismire* swallow up a whale,
I saw a raging Sea brim full of ale,
I saw a Venice Glass sixteen foot deep,
I saw a Well full of men's tears that weep,
I saw their Eyes all in a flame of fire,
I saw a House as big as the moon and higher,
I saw the Sun even in the midst of night,
I saw the Man that saw this without sight.

***Anon.***

**A pismire is an ant.*

# I Dream of a Place

I dream of a place where I long to live always:
Green hills, shallow sand dunes, and nearing the sea;

The house is of stone; there are twelve lattice windows,
And a door, with a keyhole – though lost is the key.

Thick-thatched is the roof; it has low, white-washed chimneys,
Where doves preen their wings, and coo, *Please*, love: love *me!*

There martins are flitting; the sun shines; the moon shines;
Drifts of bright flowers are adrone with the bee;

And a wonderful music of bird-song at daybreak
Wells up from the bosom of every tree.

A brook of clear water encircles the garden,
With kingcups, and cress, and the white *fleur de lys* –

Moorhens and dabchicks; the wild duck at evening
Wing away to the sun, in the shape of a V;

And the night shows the stars, shining in at the windows,
Brings nearer the far-away sigh of the sea.

Oh, the quiet, the green of the grass, the grey willows,
The light, and the shine, and the air sweet and free! –

That dream of a place where I long to live always:
Low hills, shallow sand dunes – at peace there to be!

***Walter de la Mare***

# In Daylight Strange

It was last Friday at ten to four I
Thought of the lion walking into the playground.
I was sitting, thinking, at our table when
The thought of the lion simply came,
And the sun was very hot, and the lion
Was in the yard (in daylight strange, because
Lions go out at night). He was
An enormous, sudden lion and he
Appeared just like that and was crossing very
Slowly the dusty playground, looking
To neither side, coming towards the door. He was
Coloured a yellow that was nearly grey, or a
Grey that was nearly yellow. He was so
Quiet that only I could hear the huge feet
Solidly pacing, and at the playground door he
Stopped, and looked powerfully in. There was
A forest following him, out in the street,
And noises of parakeets. When he stopped,
Looking like a picture of a lion in the frame
Of the open door, his eyes looked on at
Everything inside with a stern, curious look, he
Didn't seem completely to understand. So
He waited a second or two before
He roared. All the reeds on the river bank
Trembled, a thousand feet
Scattered among the trees, birds rose in clouds
But no one jumped in the classroom, no one screamed,

No one ran to ring the firebell, and
Miss Wolfenden went on writing on the board.
It was just exactly as if
They hadn't heard at all, as if nobody had heard.
And yet I had heard, certainly,
Yes. I had heard,
And I didn't jump.
And would you say you were surprised? Because
You ought not to be surprised.
Why should I be frightened when it was
Because *I* thought of the lion, that the lion was there?

***Alan Brownjohn***

# A Scarecrow Remembers

Head of straw and heart of wood,
With arms outstretched like this I've stood
For half a year in Hertfordshire,
My feet stuck in the mud.

Things could be worse, for I remember
One day early in November
The children came from far and wide
Wheeling a barrow with another
Ragged fellow flopped inside.
But no sooner had I glimpsed my brother
Than they took him from his carriage
To a hilltop where they perched him on a pyre
And they laughed to watch him perish
As they set his rags on fire.

The sky that night was filled with light,
With shooting stars and rockets.
I stood my ground and made no sound
When sparks fell in my pockets.

Amidst the Bedlam I could see
Old Owl a-tremble in his tree
And when the noise at last died down
The children all returned to town
And left the bonfire smouldering
And my poor brother mouldering
Till only ash remained.

***Colin West***

# A Memory

This I remember,
I saw from a train:
A shaggy wild pony
That stood in the rain.

Where I was going,
And where was the train,
I cannot remember,
I cannot explain.

All these years after
It comes back again:
A shaggy wild pony
That stood in the rain.

***Douglas Gibson***

# ideas

**1.** You can create your own strange world like that of the 'Peacock with a Fiery Tail'.
Draw a line down the middle of a piece of paper and then write a few sentences on the following pattern, using the left-hand side to name what you saw, and the right-hand side to say what it was doing or what it looked like.
For example:

**I saw a tom cat** **walking along a high brick wall.**
**I saw an old lady** **waiting for a number seven bus.**
**I saw a huge elephant** **with a long grey trunk.**

When you have finished, cut along the centre line and match the two halves of the paper to make new sentences.
For example:

**I saw an old lady** **walking along a high brick wall.**
**I saw a huge elephant** **waiting for a number seven bus.**

You will find that you create some startling, often funny, exciting images by playing with sentences in this way.

**2.** What do you remember? Think back over your life and choose one of your memories to write about. It might help you to get ideas if you work with a partner first. Spend some time just talking together, telling each other about any special memories you have. Telling someone else often helps you to remember the details you will need in order to write your poem. It can jog your memory too.

# The Family of Man

In this section are poems about people. Some of them are members of families – brothers, sisters, parents, grandparents – and others are people you might see around your neighbourhood.

## My Dad, Your Dad

My dad's fatter than your dad,
Yes, my dad's fatter than yours:
If he eats any more he won't fit in the house,
He'll have to live out of doors.

*Yes, but my dad's balder than your dad,*
*My dad's balder, OK,*
*He's only got two hairs left on his head*
*And both are turning grey.*

Ah, but my dad's thicker than your dad,
My dad's thicker all right.
He has to look at his watch to see
If it's noon or the middle of the night.

*Yes, but my dad's more boring than your dad.*
*If he ever starts counting sheep*
*When he can't get to sleep at night, he finds*
*It's the sheep that go to sleep.*

But my dad doesn't mind your dad.
*Mine quite likes yours too.*
I suppose they don't always think much of US!
*That's true, I suppose, that's true.*

***Kit Wright***

# Listn Big Brodda Dread, Na!

My sista is younga than me.
My sista outsmart five-foot-three.
My sista is own car repairer
and yu nah catch me doin judo with her.

I sey I wohn get a complex.
I wohn get a complex.
Then I see the muscles my sista flex.

My sista is tops at disco dance.
My sista is well into self-reliance.
My sista plays guitar and drums
and wahn see her knock back double rums.

I sey I wohn get a complex.
I wohn get a complex.
Then I see the muscles my sista flex.

My sista doesn mind smears of grease and dirt.
My sista'll reduce yu with sheer muscle hurt.
My sista says no guy goin keep her phone-bound
– with own car mi sista is a wheel-hound.

I sey I wohn get a complex.
I wohn get a complex.
Then I see the muscles my sista flex.

*James Berry*

## Lineage

My grandmothers were strong.
They followed plows and bent to toil.
They moved through fields sowing seed.
They touched earth and grain grew.
They were full of sturdiness and singing.
My grandmothers were strong.

My grandmothers are full of memories
Smelling of soap and onions and wet clay
With veins rolling roughly over quick hands
They have many clean words to say.
My grandmothers were strong.
Why am I not as they?

*Margaret Walker*

## Sergeant Brown's Parrot

Many policemen wear upon their shoulders
Cunning little radios. To pass away the time
They talk about the traffic to them, listen to the news,
And it helps them to Keep Down Crime.

But Sergeant Brown, he wears upon his shoulder
A tall green parrot as he's walking up and down
And all the parrot says is "Who's-a-pretty-boy-then?"
"I am," says Sergeant Brown.

*Kit Wright*

## The Miner

There are countless tons of rock above his head,
And gases wait in secret corners for a spark;
And his lamp shows dimly in the dust.
His leather belt is warm and moist with sweat,
And he crouches against the hanging coal,
And the pick swings to and fro,
And many beads of salty sweat play about his lips
And trickle down the blackened skin
To the hairy tangle on the chest.
The rats squeak and scamper among unused props,
And the fungus waxes strong.

***Idris Davies,***
from *'Gwalia Deserta'*

## The Beggar

A beggar with a ragged jacket,
And battered hat upon his head,
And matches in a little packet,
Stood on the kerb, and nothing said.
He did not even raise his eye
As on my business I went by.

If he had asked, I might have hurried;
If he had looked, I might have fled;
But just because he never worried,
And stood quite still, and nothing said,
I found I could not pass him by.
I gave, and he took, silently.

***Eleanor Farjeon***

## The Seven Ages of Man

All the world's a stage,
And all the men and women merely players;
They have their exits and their entrances,
And one man in his time plays many parts,
His acts being seven ages. At first the infant,
Mewling and puking in the nurse's arms:
And then the whining schoolboy, creeping like snail
Unwillingly to school. And then the lover,
Sighing like furnace, with a woeful ballad
Made to his mistress' eyebrow. Then, a soldier,
Full of strange oaths, and bearded like the pard,
Jealous in honour, sudden and quick in quarrel,
Seeking the bubble reputation
Even in the cannon's mouth. And then, the justice,
In fair round belly, with good capon lin'd,
With eyes severe and beard of formal cut,
Full of wise saws, and modern instances,
And so he plays his part. The sixth age shifts
Into the lean and slipper'd pantaloon,
With spectacles on nose, and pouch on side,
His youthful hose well sav'd, a world too wide
For his shrunk shank; and his big manly voice,
Turning again toward childish treble, pipes
And whistles in his sound. Last scene of all,
That ends this strange eventful history,
Is second childishness and mere oblivion;
Sans teeth, sans eyes, sans taste, sans every thing.

**_William Shakespeare,_**
from *As You Like It, Act II scene vii*

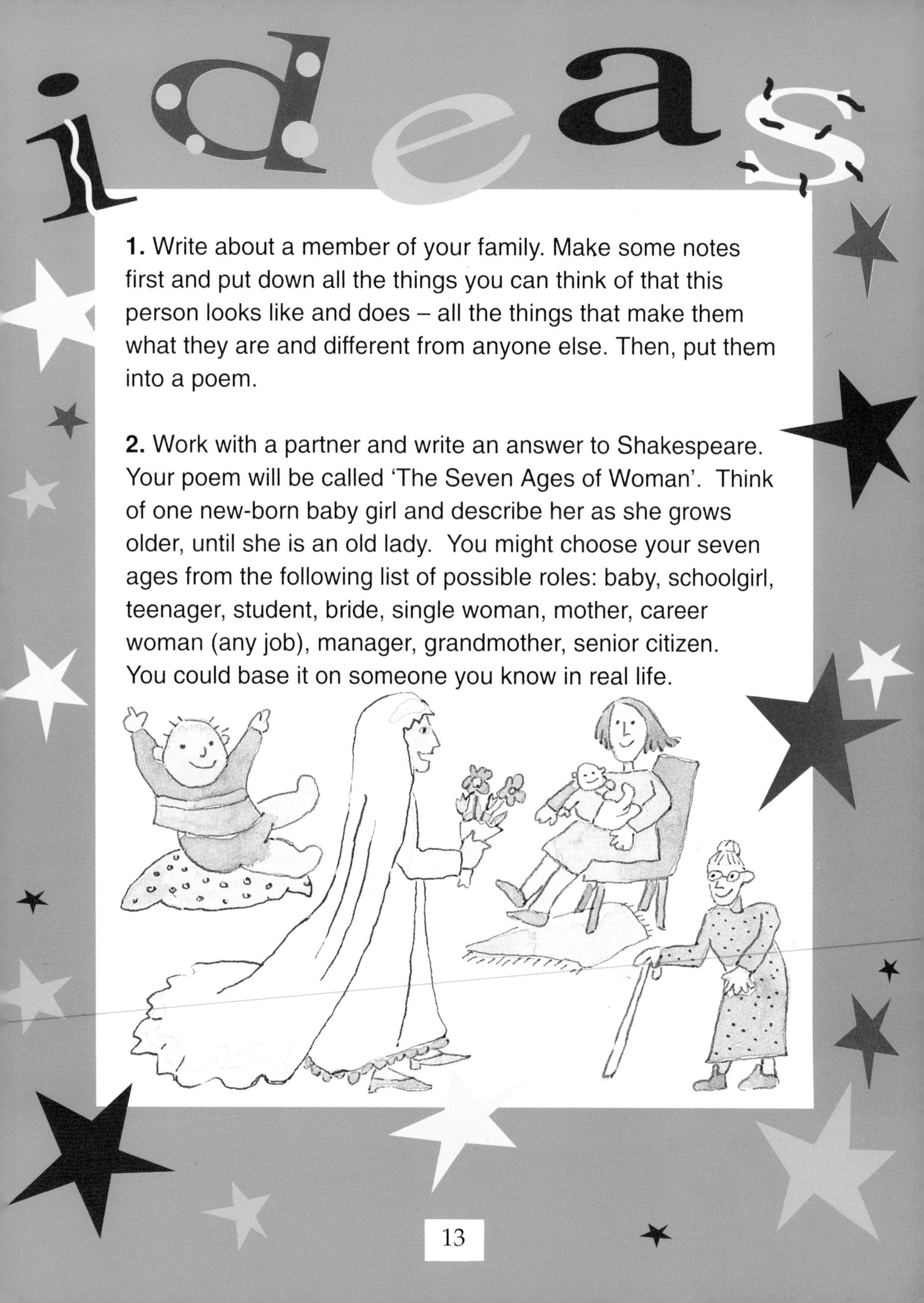

# ideas

**1.** Write about a member of your family. Make some notes first and put down all the things you can think of that this person looks like and does – all the things that make them what they are and different from anyone else. Then, put them into a poem.

**2.** Work with a partner and write an answer to Shakespeare. Your poem will be called 'The Seven Ages of Woman'. Think of one new-born baby girl and describe her as she grows older, until she is an old lady. You might choose your seven ages from the following list of possible roles: baby, schoolgirl, teenager, student, bride, single woman, mother, career woman (any job), manager, grandmother, senior citizen. You could base it on someone you know in real life.

# Fingers Crossed!

Are you superstitious? Many people are.
Here are some rhymes for curing ills or seeing into the future.
There is even a lighthearted curse that expresses our feelings sometimes when things go wrong.

## Superstitions

Wash your hands in the moonlight,
don't step on any crack;
cross your fingers,
cross your toes,
touch wood to keep your luck.

Always watch for black cats,
wear odd socks unawares;
choose sevens or threes,
"Bless you!" when you sneeze,
and never cross on stairs.

Remember these with all you've got;
if not ...

*Judith Nicholls*

## Charm for a Wart

*(Said while washing the hands in the moon's rays shining in a dry metal basin.)*

I wash my hands in this thy dish,
Oh man in the moon, do grant my wish,
And come and take away this.

***Anon.***

## Charm for a Burn or Scald

There came three angels out of the East;
One brought fire, and another brought frost,
And the third, it was the Holy Ghost.
Out fire, in frost;
In the name of the Father,
Son, and Holy Ghost.
Amen.

***Anon.***

## Winter Wise

Walk fast in snow, in frost walk slow,
And still as you go tread on your toe;
When frost and snow are both together,
Sit by the fire, and spare shoe leather.

***Traditional***

## Mirror Poem

If I look within the mirror,
Deep inside its frozen tears,
Shall I see the man I'll marry
Standing at my shoulder,
        Leaning down the years?

Shall I smile upon the mirror,
Shall my love look, smiling, back?
Midnight on Midsummer's eve:
What becomes of marriage
        If the glass should crack?

*Kit Wright*

## Traveller's Curse After Misdirection

May they stumble, stage by stage
On an endless pilgrimage,
Dawn and dusk, mile after mile,
At each and every step, a stile;
At each and every step withal
May they catch their feet and fall;
At each and every fall they take
May a bone within them break;
And may the bone that breaks within
Not be, for variation's sake,
Now rib, now thigh, now arm, now shin,
But always, without fail, THE NECK.

*Robert Graves*

## Prayer to Laughter

O Laughter
giver of relaxed mouths

you who rule our belly with tickles
you who come when not called
you who can embarrass us at times

send us stitches in our sides
shake us till the water reaches our eyes
buckle our knees till we cannot stand

we whose faces are grim and shattered
we whose hearts are no longer hearty
O Laughter we beg you

crack us up
crack us up

***John Agard***

## Prayer

From ghoulies and ghosties and long-leggedy beasties
And things that go bump in the night,
Good Lord, deliver us.

***Traditional***

## From 'All-Purpose Late Twentieth-Century Creed'

I believe in my beliefs.
It's my belief that my beliefs
Are truer far than your beliefs,
And I believe that your beliefs
Are threatening to my beliefs,
So I'm defending my beliefs
And all who hold the same beliefs
Against your dangerous beliefs
And all who share your false beliefs
Or what I think are your beliefs.
And I will die for my beliefs;
And you will die for my beliefs.

*Simon Rae*

## ideas

**1**. Write a prayer asking for protection or help to achieve something you want very much. It might be a prayer to keep you and your family safe. Or it might be one to help you be good at something, like being able to sing, to score the winning goal, or to paint the perfect picture. What do you most want at the moment?

**2.** How many superstitions do you know?
See how many your class can collect, and make a wall display of them. You can ask at home for ideas to add to the collection.

# Brush Up Your Image

All the poems here describe things in vivid pictures or images (from your **imag**ination!). Poetry can do this particularly well. The two kinds of images you will see have special names – simile and metaphor. **Similes** are comparisons in which you say one thing is like another. For example, the spaniel in 'Charlotte's Dog' has 'teeth like prongs of electric plugs'. **Metaphors** are also comparisons, but they leave out the word 'like'. They imagine that what is being described *is* something else. For example, in 'Cleaning Ladies', 'the Hoover moos and drones', and it is a 'cow with electric bones'.

## Cleaning Ladies

Belly stuffed with dust and fluff,
The Hoover moos and drones,
Grazing down on the carpet pasture:
Cow with electric bones.

Up in the tree of a chair the cat
Switches off its purr,
Stretches, blinks: a neat pink tongue
Vacuum-cleans its fur.

*Kit Wright*

# Charlotte's Dog

Daniel the spaniel has ears like rugs,
Teeth like prongs of electric plugs.

His back's a thundery winter sky,
Black clouds, white clouds rumbling by.

His nose is the rubber of an old squashed ball
Bounced in the rain. His tail you'd call

A chopped-off rope with a motor inside
That keeps it walloping. Red-rimmed-eyed,

He whimpers like plimsolls on a wooden floor.
When he yawns he closes a crimson door.

When he barks it's a shark of a sound that bites
Through frosty mornings and icy nights.

When he sleeps he wheezes on a dozing lung:
Then he wakes you too with a wash of his tongue!

*Kit Wright*

## City Lights

Huge round oranges of light
Ripen against the thin dark of the city sky,
Spilling their juice in warm pools
    on bare dry pavements.
Below them blink the traffic lights
    like the eyes of enormous cats
Crouching in the dark –
Crouching and breathing with the
    heavy purr of the traffic;
And winking tail lights slide and dart
    like goldfish
In the pale streams pouring from
    shop windows.

*Margaret Greaves*

## City Rain

After the storm
all night before
the world looked like
an upturned mop

wrung out into streets
half-dirty, half-clean,
tasting of rain
in bedraggled trees

and smelling of dog
with its shaky fur
and cold

lick.

*Kit Wright*

## Musical Chairs

Father, weighty as a minim –
Ample the armchair that has him in.

Grandma, like a semibreve,
Rests on the couch she cannot leave.

Mother, an anxious dotted crotchet
Out of the game, prefers to watch it.

Grandpa, a somewhat tiresome quaver,
Is hardly on his best behaviour.

Round him the children, demi-semis,
Fidget and tumble as they please.

The cat meanwhile lies fast asleep,
Oblivious of the times they keep.

***John Mole***

# The Beach

The beach is a quarter of golden fruit,
a soft ripe melon
sliced to a half-moon curve,
having a thick green rind
of jungle growth;
and the sea devours it
with its sharp white teeth.

*W. Hart-Smith*

**1**. Write a description of someone you know well – yourself if you like, or a friend. Describe the eyes, hands, and other features, and also how the person speaks, walks, or does other things. Each time you describe something, think what it reminds you of and then use this as your **simile**. Try to be original and not to use similes you know already. For example:
**She has large brown eyes like burnished chestnuts**
**And hair like an otter's sleek coat.**

**2**. Play the *Furniture Game* as a class. One of you thinks of someone in the room. Everybody else must try to guess who it is by asking questions. The sort of questions you ask are: What piece of furniture is this person? What animal? What time of day? What colour? What food? and so on. The person being asked must answer with the first thing that comes into mind. From the answers you should be able to guess who it is. This is a **metaphor** game. The answers are the metaphors.

# From Beginning to End

Travel can be from one place to another, or it can represent your journey through life. The poems here are about both sorts of travel. You will probably never have a journey like Zoe and her earrings, but we all have times in our lives when we have to choose which way to go, which road to take. And when we begin something new, do we always know how it will turn out in the end?



## Who?

Who is that child I see wandering, wandering
Down by the side of the quivering stream?
Why does he seem not to hear, though I call him?
Where does he come from, and what is his name?

Why do I see him at sunrise and sunset
Taking, in old-fashioned clothes, the same track?
Why, when he walks, does he cast not a shadow
Though the sun rises and falls at his back?

Why does the dust lie so thick on the hedgerow
By the great field where a horse pulls the plough?
Why do I see only meadows, where houses
Stand in a line by the riverside now?

Why does he move like a wraith by the water,
Soft as the thistledown on the breeze blown?
When I draw near him so that I may hear him,
Why does he say that his name is my own?

*Charles Causley*

## Grandad

*Grandad's dead*
*And I'm sorry about that.*

He'd a huge black overcoat.
He felt proud in it.
You could have hidden
A football crowd in it.
Far too big –
It was a lousy fit
But Grandad didn't
Mind a bit.
He wore it all winter
With a squashed black hat.

*Now he's dead*
*And I'm sorry about that.*

He'd got twelve stories.
I'd heard every one of them
Hundreds of times
But that was the fun of them:
You knew what was coming
So you could join in.
He'd got big hands
And brown, grooved skin
And when he laughed
It knocked you flat.

*Now he's dead*
*And I'm sorry about that.*

***Kit Wright***

## Zoe's Earrings

She bought 'em in the autumn
After spotting 'em in Nottingham.
She took 'em home to Cookham
And she put 'em in a drawer

Till May came and the day came
When she wore 'em down to Shoreham,
But *nobody* was for 'em
So she wore 'em nevermore ...

Till the wedding of her sister
To a mister out at Bicester,
Name of Jimmy, who said, "*Gimme*,"
So without 'em she went home,

But she nipped back down to nick 'em
For a knees-up in High Wycombe,
For an evening quite near Chevening
And a dawn at Kilmacolm.

They were in 'er for a dinner
Which was excellent, in Pinner,
And another one, a cracker,
In Majacca – that's in Spain –

Then she popped 'em on in Haddenham
And didn't feel too bad in 'em:
She felt in 'em, in Cheltenham,
Just as right as rain.

They looked smart on in Dumbarton,
They looked wizard on the Lizard,
They looked corking down in Dorking
And incredible in Crewe.

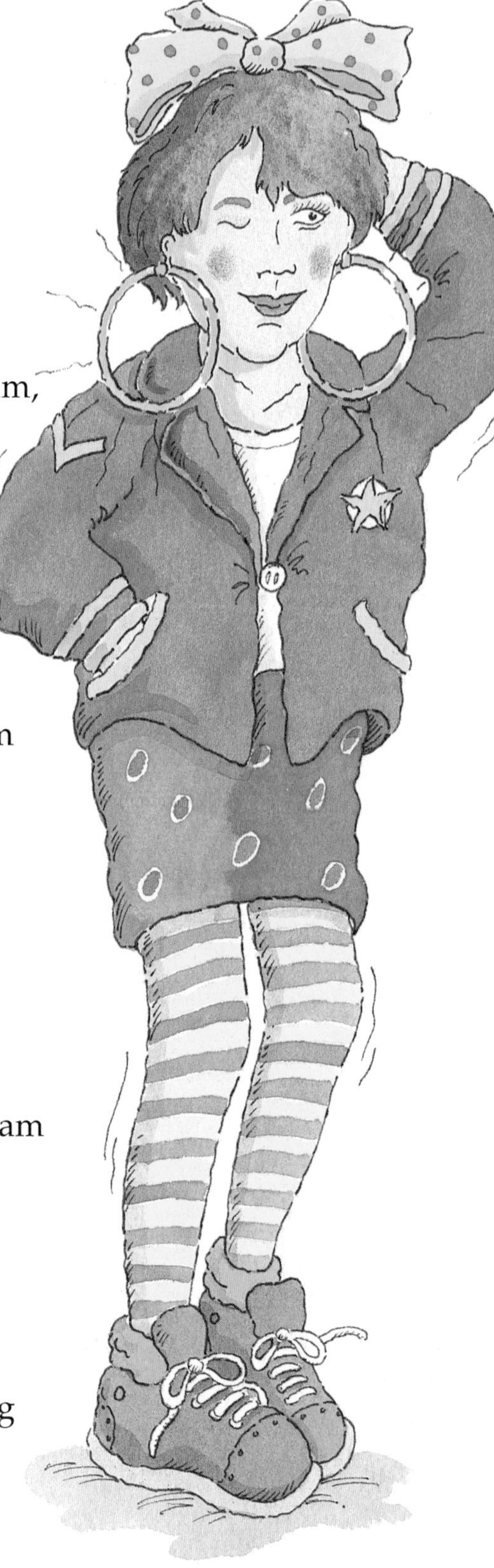

When she wore 'em into Rugely
They impressed the people hugely,
While in Fordham folk adored 'em,
And they *loved* 'em in West Looe!

The citizens of Kettering
Had never seen a better ring,
In fact no better pair of 'em –
'Take care of 'em!' they cried.

Then she slithered into Lytham with 'em,
Shaking out a rhythm with 'em,
Wobb-er-ling and jogg-er-ling
Her head from side to side.

Folk in Preston thought the best 'un
Was the right 'un. In New Brighton
And in Sefton, though, the *left* 'un
Was the one they favoured more,

While in Greenham, when they'd seen 'em,
They said, "How to choose between 'em?
What one praises in its brother,
In the *other* one is for!"

Then she tried 'em with new make-up
On a sponsored run round Bacup,
And at Norwich for a porridge-
Eating contest which she won,

But, spilling 'em in Gillingham,
Her lobes felt light in Willingham,
And nothing else is filling 'em,
So now
The poem's
Done!

***Kit Wright***

## From 'Six Young Men'

The celluloid of a photograph holds them well, –
Six young men, familiar to their friends.
Four decades that have faded and ochre-tinged
This photograph have not wrinkled the faces or the hands.
Though their cocked hats are not now fashionable,
Their shoes shine. One imparts an intimate smile,
One chews a grass, one lowers his eyes, bashful,
One is ridiculous with cocky pride –
Six months after this picture they were all dead.

*Ted Hughes*

## The Tree and the Pool

"I don't want my leaves to drop," said the tree.
"I don't want to freeze," said the pool.
"I don't want to smile," said the sombre man,
"Or ever to cry," said the Fool.

"I don't want to open," said the bud.
"I don't want to end," said the night.
"I don't want to rise," said the neap-tide,
"Or ever to fall," said the kite.

They wished and they murmured and they whispered,
They said that to change was a crime,
Then a voice from nowhere answered,
"You must do what I say," said Time.

*Brian Patten*

# ideas

**1**. Have you known someone who has died? Or perhaps you had a pet which died? You may once have known someone who has now moved away and you don't see them any more. It can often help us to accept that they are no longer with us if we write about the person. It can be a celebration of that person's or animal's life.
Read Kit Wright's 'Grandad' again and notice the details he has used. Then write your own poem remembering someone and telling about the things that made them special, the little details you remember most.

**2.** Roads have often been a favourite *metaphor* for life. Life is seen as a journey and words to do with roads can help to describe how life might be lived. Words like crossroads, junction, narrow lane, wide highway, distance, bridge and so on become part of the metaphor.
Imagine you are travelling on a road and reach a fork where the road goes in two different directions. Which way will you go? What do you see ahead on each of the possible ways? What kinds of roads are they? Can you see into the distance, or are there corners? Describe what you see and how you choose. Do you go on, or do you go back, and what happens?

# Rhythm Section

All the poems here use different strong rhythms and patterns to make them sing. Poetry is related to music and song, and rhythm can be very important in helping a poem to tell its story. Most poems should be read aloud, and these ones definitely should. When you read them, you should be able to hear the beat behind the words and it will carry you along – but don't forget to think about the meaning of the poems as you say them. Read for the sense and the rhythm will come through on its own.

## From **'The Destruction of Sennacherib'**

The Assyrian came down like the wolf on the fold,
And his cohorts were gleaming in purple and gold;
And the sheen of their spears was like stars on the sea,
When the blue wave rolls nightly on deep Galilee.

Like the leaves of the forest when Summer is green,
That host with their banners at sunset were seen:
Like the leaves of the forest when Autumn hath blown,
That host on the morrow lay withered and strown.

For the Angel of Death spread his wings on the blast,
And breathed in the face of the foe as he passed;
And the eyes of the sleepers waxed deadly and chill,
And their hearts but once heaved, and for ever grew still!

***George Gordon, Lord Byron***

# From **'Night Mail'**

This is the night mail crossing the border,
Bringing the cheque and the postal order,

Letters for the rich, letters for the poor,
The shop at the corner and the girl next door.

Pulling up Beattock, a steady climb –
The gradient's against her, but she's on time.

Past cotton-grass and moorland boulder,
Shovelling white steam over her shoulder,

Snorting noisily, she passes
Silent miles of wind-bent grasses.

Birds turn their heads as she approaches,
Stare from bushes at her blank-faced coaches.

Sheep-dogs cannot turn her course;
They slumber on with paws across.

In the farm she passes no one wakes,
But a jug in the bedroom gently shakes.

***W.H. Auden***

# From **'The Song of Hiawatha'**

Swift of foot was Hiawatha;
He could shoot an arrow from him,
And run forward with such fleetness,
That the arrow fell behind him!
Strong of arm was Hiawatha;
He could shoot ten arrows upward,
Shoot them with such strength and swiftness,
That the tenth had left the bow-string
Ere the first to earth had fallen!
He had mittens, Minjekahwun,
Magic mittens made of deer-skin;
When upon his hands he wore them,
He could smite the rocks asunder,
He could grind them into powder.
He had moccasins enchanted,
Magic moccasins of deer-skin;
When he bound them round his ankles,
When upon his feet he tied them,
At each stride a mile he measured!

***Henry Wadsworth Longfellow***

# Mama Dot

Born on a sunday
in the kingdom of Ashante

Sold on monday
into slavery

Ran away on tuesday
cause she born free

Lost a foot on wednesday
when they catch she

Worked all thursday
till her head grey

Dropped on friday
where they burned she

Freed on saturday
in a new century

***Fred D'Aguiar***

# Sailing Homeward

Cliffs that rise a thousand feet
Without a break,
Lake that stretches a hundred miles
Without a wave,
Sands that are white through all the year
Without a stain,
Pine-tree woods, winter and summer
Ever-green,
Streams that forever flow and flow
Without a pause,
Trees that for twenty thousand years
Your vows have kept,
You have suddenly healed the pain of a traveller's heart,
And moved his brush to write a new song.

***Chan Fang-Sheng,***
*translated from the Chinese by Arthur Waley*

# Cargoes

Quinquireme of Nineveh from distant Ophir
Rowing home to haven in sunny Palestine,
With a cargo of ivory,
And apes and peacocks,
Sandalwood, cedarwood, and sweet white wine.

Stately Spanish galleon coming from the Isthmus,
Dipping through the Tropics by the palm-green shores,
With a cargo of diamonds,
Emeralds, amethysts,
Topazes, and cinnamon, and gold moidores.

Dirty British coaster with a salt-caked smoke stack
Butting through the Channel in the mad March days,
With a cargo of Tyne coal,
Road-rail, pig-lead,
Firewood, iron-ware, and cheap tin trays.

*John Masefield*

# Nine Lives

## (In memoriam Thisbe 1976-1990)

This is my grave by the holly tree,
Remember me?

I am the cat who arrived by rail
Without a tail.

I am the cat who tried walking on water
Which would not support her.

I am the cat who got stuck on the ledge
Too near the edge.

I am the cat who was locked in the shed
And could not be fed.

I am the cat who ran in the road
Where traffic flowed.

I am the cat who spat in the night
And lost the fight.

I am the cat who hid out in the snow
When you wanted to go.

I am the cat who with arthritic bones
Concealed her groans.

I am the cat who that Autumn day
Just faded away.

This is my grave by the holly tree.
Remember me.

*Sandra Willingham*

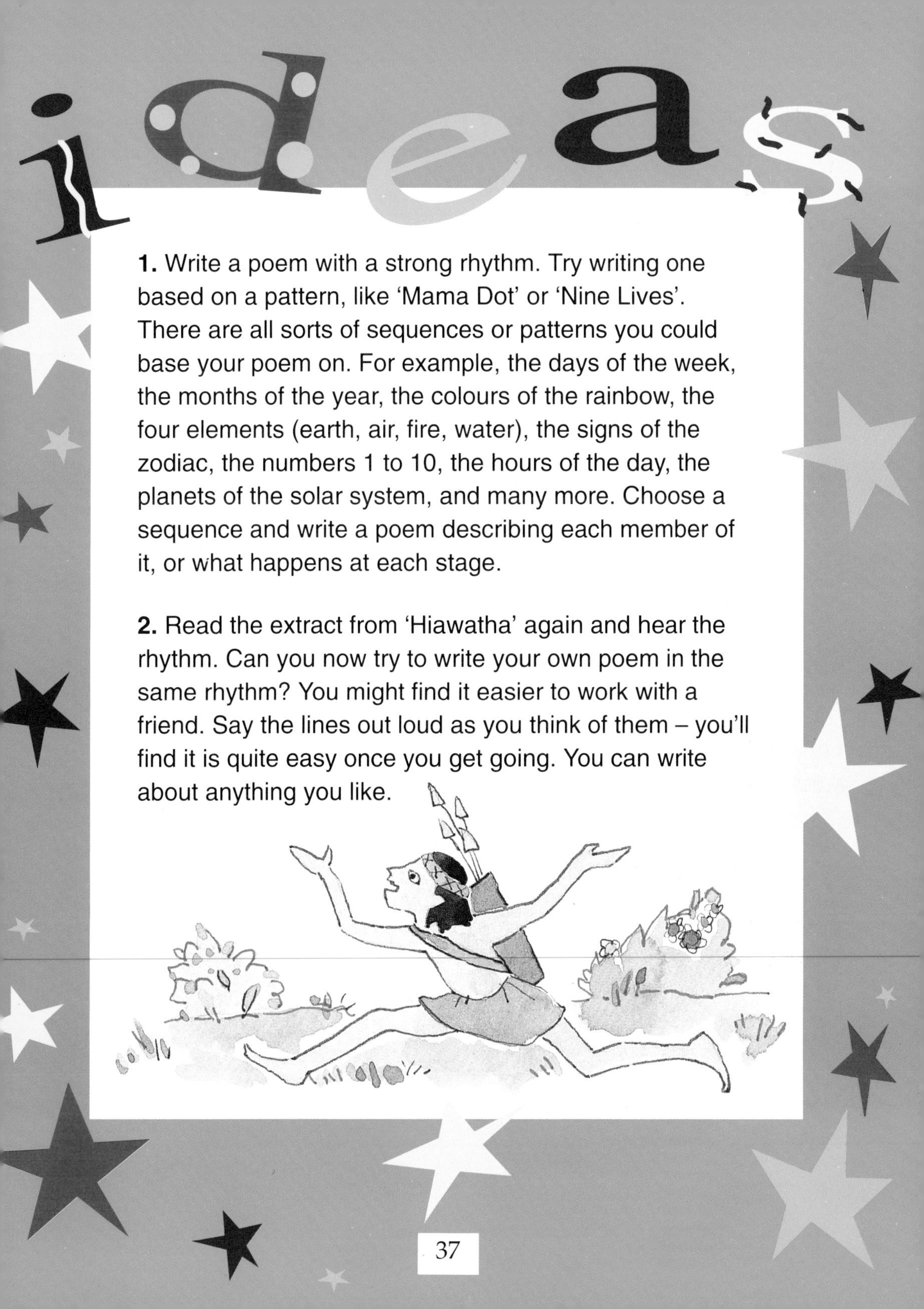

# ideas

**1.** Write a poem with a strong rhythm. Try writing one based on a pattern, like 'Mama Dot' or 'Nine Lives'. There are all sorts of sequences or patterns you could base your poem on. For example, the days of the week, the months of the year, the colours of the rainbow, the four elements (earth, air, fire, water), the signs of the zodiac, the numbers 1 to 10, the hours of the day, the planets of the solar system, and many more. Choose a sequence and write a poem describing each member of it, or what happens at each stage.

**2.** Read the extract from 'Hiawatha' again and hear the rhythm. Can you now try to write your own poem in the same rhythm? You might find it easier to work with a friend. Say the lines out loud as you think of them – you'll find it is quite easy once you get going. You can write about anything you like.

# Taking the Mickey

It can be great fun writing new words to familiar tunes or rhymes. You probably know some playground rhymes which do this. Many poets have enjoyed writing this kind of verse, which is called **parody**. Some of the parodies here are of famous poems, and you will recognise the 'Hiawatha' parody from the poem in the previous chapter. Parodies are meant to be enjoyed, so read on.

## Oh dear!

Oh dear, what can the matter be?
Three old ladies were stuck in the lavatory;
They were there from Monday to Saturday –
Nobody knew they were there!

*Anon.*

## While shepherds ...

While shepherds washed their socks by night,
All seated round the tub;
A bar of Sunlight soap came down
And they began to scrub.

*Anon.*

## Twinkle, twinkle

Twinkle, twinkle, little bat!
How I wonder what you're at!
Up above the world you fly,
Like a tea-tray in the sky.

*Lewis Carroll*

## Mary 1

Mary had a little lamb
Its feet as black as soot,
And into Mary's bread and jam
Its sooty foot it put.

*Anon.*

## Mary 2

Mary had a little lamb
Her father shot it dead,
And now it goes to school with her
Between two chunks of bread.

*Anon.*

## Mary 3

Mary had a little bear
To which she was so kind
That everywhere dear Mary went
You saw her bear running along beside her.

*Anon.*

## From **'All Things Dull and Ugly'**

All things dull and ugly
All creatures short and squat
All things rude and nasty
The Lord God made the lot.

Each little snake that poisons
Each little wasp that stings
He made their brutish venom
He made their horrid wings.

*Monty Python*

## From **'The Charge of the Light Brigade'**

Half a league, half a league,
Half a league onward,
All in the valley of Death
Rode the six hundred.
"Forward, the Light Brigade!
Charge for the guns!" he said:
Into the valley of Death
Rode the six hundred.

"Forward, the Light Brigade!"
Was there a man dismay'd?
Not tho' the soldiers knew
Someone had blunder'd:
Theirs not to make reply,
Theirs not to reason why,
Theirs but to do and die:
Into the valley of Death
Rode the six hundred.

Cannon to the right of them,
Cannon to the left of them,
Cannon in front of them
Volley'd and thunder'd;
Storm'd at with shot and shell,
Boldly they rode and well,
Into the jaws of Death,
Into the mouth of Hell
Rode the six hundred.

***Alfred, Lord Tennyson***

## The Charge of the Mouse Brigade

Half an inch, half an inch,
Half an inch onward,
Into Cat Valley
Rode the Six Hundred.

"Forward the Mouse Brigade!
Ravage their fleas!" he said.
"Capture the cheese!" he said.
Onward they thundered.

Claws to the right of them.
Claws to the left of them.
Claws to the front of them.
Pounces unnumbered.

Crash! – through the Catty flanks!
Shattered their fishy ranks!
Captured the Cheddar! thanks
To the Mouse Brigade!
Noble Six Hundred.

*Bernard Stone*

# The Modern Hiawatha

When he killed the Mudjokivis,
Of the skin he made him mittens,
Made them with the fur side inside,
Made them with the skin side outside,
He, to get the warm side inside,
Put the inside skin side outside.
He, to get the cold side outside,
Put the warm side fur side inside.
That's why he put the fur side inside,
Why he put the skin side outside,
Why he turned them inside outside.

*George A. Strong*

Try writing your own parody of a rhyme or song you know well. It might be a nursery rhyme, or a song you sing at school. Working with a partner can make it more fun and help you both to get ideas on how to do it.
In a parody of this kind you obviously keep some of the original lines and phrases, while changing other parts to make it funny.

# A Tale to Tell

This long poem is very famous and tells a tragic story. Like all good stories, it is meant to be listened to; so why not read it out loud to each other. Picture the highwayman riding over the purple moor, and imagine what was going through the mind of Bess, the landlord's daughter.

## The Highwayman

The wind was a torrent of darkness among the gusty trees,
The moon was a ghostly galleon tossed upon cloudy seas,
The road was a ribbon of moonlight over the purple moor,
And the highwayman came riding –
Riding – riding –
The highwayman came riding up to the old inn door.

He'd a French cocked-hat on his forehead, a bunch of lace at his chin,
A coat of claret velvet, and breeches of brown doe-skin;
They fitted with never a wrinkle: his boots were up to the thigh!
And he rode with a jewelled twinkle,
His pistol butts a-twinkle,
His rapier hilt a-twinkle, under the jewelled sky.

Over the cobbles he clattered and clashed in the dark inn-yard,
And he tapped with his whip on the shutters, but all was locked and barred;
He whistled a tune to the window, and who should be waiting there
But the landlord's black-eyed daughter,
Bess, the landlord's daughter,
Plaiting a dark red love-knot into her long black hair.

And dark in the dark old inn-yard a stable-wicket creaked
Where Tim the ostler listened; his face was white and peaked;
His eyes were hollows of madness, his hair like mouldy hay,
But he loved the landlord's daughter,
The landlord's red-lipped daughter;
Dumb as a dog he listened, as he heard the robber say –

"One kiss, my bonny sweetheart, I'm after a prize tonight,
But I shall be back with the yellow gold before the morning light;
Yet, if they press me sharply, and harry me through the day,
Then look for me by moonlight,
Watch for me by moonlight,
I'll come to thee by moonlight, though hell should bar the way."

He rose upright in the stirrups; he scarce could reach her hand,
But she loosened her hair i' the casement! His face burnt like a brand
As the black cascade of perfume came tumbling over his breast;
And he kissed its waves in the moonlight,
(Oh, sweet black waves in the moonlight!)
Then he tugged at his rein in the moonlight, and galloped away to the West.

# Part Two

He did not come in the dawning; he did not come at noon;
And out o' the tawny sunset, before the rise o' the moon,
When the road was a gypsy's ribbon, looping the purple moor,
A red-coat troop came marching –
Marching – marching –
King George's men came marching, up to the old inn door.

They said no word to the landlord, they drank his ale instead,
But they gagged his daughter and bound her to the foot of her narrow bed;
Two of them knelt at her casement, with muskets at their side!
There was death at every window;
And hell at one dark window;
For Bess could see, through the casement, the road that *he* would ride.

They had tied her up to attention, with many a sniggering jest;
They had bound a musket beside her, with the barrel beneath her breast!
"Now keep good watch!" and they kissed her. She heard the dead man say –
*Look for me by moonlight;*
*Watch for me by moonlight;*
*I'll come to thee by moonlight, though hell should bar the way!*

She twisted her hands behind her; but all the knots held good!
She writhed her hands till her fingers were wet with sweat or blood!
They stretched and strained in the darkness, and the hours crawled by like years,
Till now, on thc stroke of midnight,
Cold, on the stroke of midnight,
The tip of one finger touched it! The trigger at least was hers!

The tip of one finger touched it; she strove no more for the rest!
Up, she stood to attention, with the barrel beneath her breast,
She would not risk their hearing; she would not strive again;
For the road lay bare in the moonlight;
Blank and bare in the moonlight;
And the blood of her veins in the moonlight throbbed to her love's refrain.

*Tlot-tlot; tlot-tlot!* Had they heard it? The horse-hoofs ringing clear;
*Tlot-tlot; tlot-tlot,* in the distance? Were they deaf that they did not hear?
Down the ribbon of moonlight, over the brow of the hill,
The highwayman came riding,
Riding, riding!
The red-coats looked to their priming! She stood up, straight and still!

*Tlot-tlot,* in the frosty silence! *Tlot-tlot,* in the echoing night!
Nearer he came and nearer! Her face was like a light!
Her eyes grew wide for a moment; she drew one last deep breath,
Then her finger moved in the moonlight,
Her musket shattered the moonlight,
Shattered her breast in the moonlight and warned him – with her death.

He turned; he spurred to the Westward; he did not know who stood
Bowed, with her head o'er the musket, drenched with her own red blood!
Not till the dawn he heard it, and slowly blanched to hear
How Bess, the landlord's daughter,
The landlord's black-eyed daughter,
Had watched for her love in the moonlight, and died in the darkness there.

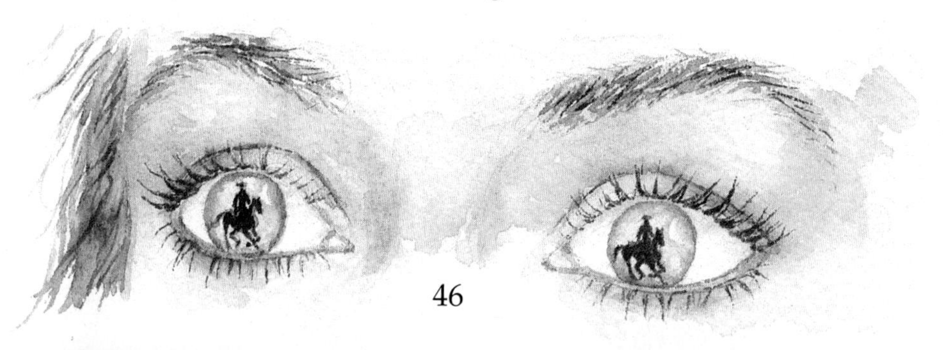

Back, he spurred like a madman, shrieking a curse to the sky,
With the white road smoking behind him and his rapier brandished high!
Blood-red were his spurs i' the golden noon; wine-red was his velvet coat;
When they shot him down on the highway,
                    Down like a dog on the highway,
And he lay in his blood on the highway, with a bunch of lace at his throat.

*And still of a winter's night, they say, when the wind is in the trees,*
*When the moon is a ghostly galleon tossed upon cloudy seas,*
*When the road is a ribbon of moonlight over the purple moor,*
*A highwayman comes riding –*
                    *Riding – riding –*
*A highwayman comes riding, up to the old inn-door.*

*Over the cobbles he clatters and clangs in the dark inn-yard;*
*And he taps with his whip on the shutters, but all is locked and barred;*
*He whistles a tune to the window, and who should be waiting there*
*But the landlord's black-eyed daughter,*
                    *Bess, the landlord's daughter,*
*Plaiting a dark red love-knot into her long black hair.*

***Alfred Noyes***

# Index